FELIX MENDELSSOHN BARTHOLDY

SYMPHONY No. 4

A major/A-Dur/La majeur
Op. 90
"Italian"

Edited by/Herausgegeben von
Roger Fiske

Ernst Eulenburg Ltd
London · Mainz · New York · Tokyo · Zürich

FELIX MENDELSSOHN-BARTHOLDY

Symphony No. 4 in A major, The 'Italian'

In 1830 when he was twenty-one Mendelssohn had as many as three symphonies on the stocks. In the previous summer he had found the beginning of his *Scotch* Symphony in Holyrood Palace, Edinburgh, and in the winter of 1829-30 he quickly wrote his *Reformation* Symphony for the 300th anniversary of the Augsburg 'Confession', and by the end of 1830 he had begun sketching his *Italian* Symphony in Rome. The Augsburg celebrations were postponed for political reasons, and when a little later the *Reformation* Symphony was scheduled for performance in Paris the orchestra so disliked the work that the performance was cancelled. Mendelssohn was much distressed by this set-back and determined never again to release a symphony without giving it all possible thought. He took twelve years to get the *Scotch* Symphony to his liking, and he never did feel that he had finished the *Italian*, which was still unpublished at his death in 1847 and, in Germany, unperformed.

Mendelssohn's father had a profound belief in the benefits of travel. Having financed his son's Scottish trip in 1829 he encouraged the Italian one in the autumn of 1830. After brief stays in Venice and Florence Mendelssohn reached Rome on 1 November and spent the winter there. He met Berlioz with whom he had a number of musical discussions. In Mediterranean surroundings he found it impossible to make progress with his *Scotch* Symphony and by the early spring of 1831 he was concentrating on the *Italian*. 'It will be the jolliest piece I've so far written', he reported to his father on 22 February. He left the slow movement until the summer when he was in Naples and finished the first version of the whole work on 13 March 1833, by which time he had been back in Northern Europe some eighteen months. He was pushed into finishing his symphony by an offer of one hundred guineas from the Philharmonic Society of London (this to include two other works as well) and he conducted the first performance in London on 13 May 1833. A later London performance was conducted by Moscheles, but Mendelssohn was not satisfied with the work and a revised version was heard there on 18 June 1838. Still dissatisfied he made yet more alterations and seemed averse to any performances being given in his native land.

Mendelssohn was very conscious of following in the footsteps of the great classical symphonists, and it may be that he hesitated to offer to the public in definitive form so light-hearted a work until he had first established the seriousness of his intentions with the *Scotch* Symphony. Later, as he approached middle-age, he may have felt he had outgrown the carefree youthfulness of the music. However that may be, the *Italian* Symphony was not heard in Germany until 1 November 1849, two years after Mendelssohn's death, when a performance was conducted in Leipzig by Julius Rietz, his successor as conductor of the Gewandhaus Orchestra. Breitkopf & Härtel published a score in 1851 and another in 1875 as part of the Complete Works series. This last is still the standard performing score. The autograph, which shows numerous alterations, is in Berlin's Deutsche Staatsbibliothek, as are most surviving Mendelssohn autographs.

The *Italian* Symphony is very unusual in starting in the major and ending in the minor; in this it resembles Haydn's *Emperor* Quartet, Op. 76 no. 3. In the first movement both the main subjects feature a falling third, and there are occasional hints of the first subject in augmentation, for instance on the clarinet in bar 159. The number and quality of the first-time bars makes the repeat especially desirable. A new theme in the development (Vl.II, bar 225) recurs in the coda. As in other Mendelssohn symphonies the recapitulation is only half the length of the exposition and almost all newly-composed. The return of the second subject with the cellos and violas in thirds recalls a similar orchestral device in the second movement of the *Reformation* Symphony. The slow movement is said to represent a Pilgrims' March; Mendelssohn may well have seen pilgrims near the Abruzzi Mountains between Rome and Naples as did Berlioz, who at about the same time was including a Pilgrims' March in *Harold in Italy*. Moscheles thought the main tune was a genuine pilgrims' song from Bohemia, but had this been so Mendelssohn would not have altered it when revising the symphony. The tune is very like Zelter's setting of Goethe's 'Es was ein König in Thule', which Mendelssohn must have known, but the likeness is probably a coincidence. There is virtually no recapitulation; the form of the movement is very original. In his third movement Mendelssohn returned to the old-world grace of the slow Minuet though without so naming it. He did this in no other work of his maturity. The trio section may owe its lay-out to the Trio in Beethoven's Fourth Symphony, but if so the device has been transformed into something magically new. The Saltarello was inspired by some Neapolitan girls Mendelssohn saw dancing at Amalfi a few miles south of Naples; he was there on 31 May 1831, as we know from the date on his exquisite pencil sketch of the little town and its mountain background in the Bodleian Library, Oxford. In bars 238-44 the woodwind come very close to quoting the main first-movement theme.

This score follows the one in the Complete Works series (referred to below as **B**) which itself follows the 1851 publication (**A**) except that it sometimes adds apparently-intended expression marks missing in **A**. For instance:

I 350-53, Ob: *cresc.* and *dim.* symbol; 388, Ob: *sf.*

II 61-2, Ob/Fg: slur (yet no slurs in 10-11, 18-19 etc.); 82, Vc/Cb: slur.

III 23 & 149, Ob: slur.

IV 37, Cor:*sf* (A has>); 37-41, Ww: *sf* three times in each part; 229, Ww: slur.

Editorial additions are in square brackets; there are very few. Some expression marks in **A** and **B** which can hardly have been intended have been cut:

I 349 Cb: *pp*. 376, Vla/Vc/Cb: *p*; 527, Fl I: *p* (surely meant for Fl II in 528); 531, Vl II, n2:>.

IV 23, Ob II, n2: *cresc.*

All or most of these were probably left-overs from the first version. Perhaps Vla's slur and staccato dot in **II** 67 should be cut as they are not in the Ob/Fg parts in this bar or in any similar bars, but Mendelssohn might have added them elsewhere later. He never decided whether the main Finale theme should be staccato or slurred, being perhaps uncertain if it were playable staccato on woodwind at the very fast tempo. Bars 6-7 imply staccato up to 32, but in 80-1 he suddenly slurs Cl and Fg. Should Fl be slurred too in 80? Or from 76? Or not at all? He did give Fl slurs in 110-1 but **B** cuts them, perhaps because Cl is unslurred in 106-8. Yet **B** slurs Ob in 115-7 though **A** has only the first of these slurs. In 255-61 both **A** and **B** slur Fl, but only **B** has the first three slurs for Cl. It is for conductors to achieve consistency if they so wish. Mendelssohn was meticulously careful about such details but it must be remembered that he never prepared his autograph for publication.

Roger Fiske, 1979

FELIX MENDELSSOHN-BARTHOLDY

Sinfonie Nr.4 in A-Dur ('Italienische Sinfonie')

Als Mendelssohn 1830 einundzwanzig Jahre alt war, hatter er nicht weniger als drei Sinfonien in Vorbereitung. Im Sommer des Vorjahres hatte er den Anfang zu seiner *Schottischen* Sinfonie im Holyrood Palast zu Edinburgh gefunden, im Winter 1829-30 schrieb er eilig seine *Reformationssinfonie* zum dreihundersten Jahrestag der ‚Augsburgischen Konfession', und schliesslich, gegen Ende 1830, hatte er mit den Skizzen zu seiner *Italienischen* Sinfonie begonnen. Aus politischen Gründen wurden die Augsburger Festlichkeiten verschoben, und als bald darauf die *Reformationssinfonie* in Paris aufgeführt werden sollte, missfiel sie dem Orchester so sehr, dass die Aufführung abgesagt wurde. Mendelssohn war durch diesen Rückschlag so verzweifelt, dass er beschloss, nie wieder eine Sinfonie freizugeben, ohne vorher alles bis ins letzte erwägt zu haben. Es dauerte zwölf Jahre, bis ihm die *Schottische* Sinfonie so gelang, wie er es wünschte, und er konnte sich nie davon überzeugen, dass er seine *Italienische* Sinfonie wirklich vollendet hatte; so war auch dieses Werk, als er 1847 starb, weder veröffentlicht, noch in Deutschland aufgeführt worden.

Mendelssohns Vater glaubte fest an die Nützlichkeit des Reisens. 1829 hatte er die Reise seines Sohnes nach Schottland finanziert, und er ermutigte ihn auch dazu, im Herbst 1830 nach Italien zu fahren. Nach kurzen Aufenthalten in Venedig und Florenz, kam Mendelssohn am 1. November in Rom an, wo er den Winter verbrachte. Dort traf er Berlioz, mit dem er mehrmals über Musik sprach. In einer für das Mittelmeer typischen Umgebung war es ihm unmöglich, mit seiner *Schottischen* Sinfonie Fortschritte zu machen, und zu Anfang des Frühlings von 1831 hatte er sich schon auf die Arbeit an seiner *Italienischen* Sinfonie konzentriert. Am 22. Februar schrieb er an seinen Vater: „Es wird das lustigste Stück, das ich gemacht habe." Den langsamen Satz schrieb er erst im Sommer in Neapel, und die erste Fassung des ganzen Werks wurde am 13. März 1833 fertig, nachdem er schon wieder ungefähr achtzehn Monate in Nordeuropa verbracht hatte. Ein Angebot von hundert Guineen durch die Londoner Philharmonische Gesellschaft (einschliesslich zweier weiteren, neuen Werke) veranlasste ihn, seine Sinfonie zu vollenden. Er dirigierte selbst die Erstaufführung in London am 13. Mai 1833. Später dirigierte Moscheles noch eine Aufführung in London, aber Mendelssohn war mit der Komposition nicht zufrieden, und eine überarbeitete Fassung wurde in der gleichen Stadt am 18. Juni 1838 aufgeführt. Allein, da er immer noch nicht zufrieden war, nahm er weitere Änderungen vor und schien sich Aufführungen in seinem Vaterland zu widersetzen.

Mendelssohn war wich durchaus bewusst, ein Nachfolger der grossen klassischen Sinfoniker zu wein, und es wäre möglich, dass er desahlb zögerte dem Publikum ein so heiteres Werk in einer endgültigen Form vorzusetzen, weil er zuerst mit der *Schottischen* Sinfonie seinen künstlerischen Ernst beweisen wollte. Später, als er sich den mittleren Altersjahren näherte, mag er gefühlt haben, dass er der sorglosen Jugenlichkeit dieser Musik entwachsen war. Wie dem auch sei, die *Italienische* Sinfonie wurde in Deutschland erst am 1. November 1849, zwei Jahre nach Mendelssohns Tod, gespielt, und zwar in einer von Julius Rietz, seinem Nachfolger als Dirigent des Gewandhausorchesters, geleiteten Aufführung. Die Partitur wurde von Breitkopf & Härtel 1851 herausgegeben, und eine weitere erschien 1875 im Rahmen der Gesamtausgabe. Die letztere ist auch heute noch für Aufführungen massgebend. Das Autograph, das eine grosse Anzahl von Änderungen aufweist, befindet sich in der Deutschen Staatsbibliothek in Berlin, wo auch die meisten erhaltenen Manuskripte von Mendelssohn aufbewahrt werden.

Die *Italienische* Sinfonie ist darin höchst ungewöhnlich, dass sie in Dur beginnt und in Moll endet; sie ähnelt in dieser Beziehung Haydns *Kaiserquartett*, Op. 76 Nr. 3. Im ersten Satz haben beide Hauptthemen eine absteigende Terz als Wesenszug gemeinsam, und eine Augmentation des ersten Themas wird, wie z.B. auf der Klarinette, Takt 159, mitunter angedeutet. Die Anzahl und Feinheit der nur einmal gespielten Takte vor dem Wiederholungszeichen macht eine Wiederholung besonders wünschenswert. Ein neues Thema in der Durchführung (Vl. II, Takt 202) taucht in der Koda wieder auf. Wie in anderen Sinfonien von Mendelssohn ist die Reprise nur halb so lang wie die Exposition und fast durchweg neukomponiert. Die Wiederholung des von den Bratschen und Celli in Terzen gespielten zweiten Themas erinnert an einen ähnlichen Kompositionsvorgang im zweiten Satz der *Reformationssinfonie*. Der langsame Satz soll, so sagt man, einen Pilgermarsch vorstellen. Möglicherweise hat Mendelssohn, wie Berlioz, Pilger in der Nähe der Abruzzen zwischen Rom und Neapel gesehen, und Berlioz komponierte um ungefähr die gleiche Zeit einen Pilgermarsch für seine Sinfonie *Harold in Italien*. Moscheles war der Meinung, dass die Hauptmelodie ein echtes Pilgerlied aus Böhmen war, doch wäre dies der Fall gewesen, so hätte Mendelssohn die Melodie nicht geändert, als er die Sinfonie neu bearbeitete. Diese Melodie ist Zelters Vertonung von Goethes ‚Es war ein König in Thule' sehr ähnlich. Mendelssohn muss das Lied gekannt haben, aber die Ähnlichkeit ist warhscheinlich zufällig. Der Satz hat sozusagen keine Reprise, und seine Form ist in der Erfindung höchst originell. Im dritten Satz kehrt Mendelssohn zur anmutvollen Vergangenheit des langsamen Menuetts zurück, obwohl er das Stück nicht so bezeichnet. In keinem anderen Werk seiner reifen Jahre kommt so etwas vor. Der Trioteil mag seinen Aufbau dem Trio in Beethovens vierter Sinfonie verdanken, aber wenn dem auch so wäre, so wurde diese Form von Mendelssohn auf zauberhafte Weise neugestaltet. Die Anregung für den Saltarello empfing Mendelssohn durch ein paar tanzende Mädchen, die er in Amalfi, wenige Kilometer südlich von Neapel sah. Dort hielt er sich am 31. Mai 1831 auf, wie wir aus der Datierung auf seiner zauberhaften Bleistiftskizze von der kleinen Stadt und ihrem gebirgigen Hintergrund wissen, die sich in der Bodleian Library in Oxford befindet. In den Takten 238-44 kommen die Holzbläser einem Zitat des Hauptthemas aus dem ersten Satz sehr nah.

Roger Fiske, 1979

Deutsche Übersetzung Stefan de Haan

SYMPHONY No. 4

I

Felix Mendelssohn-Bartholdy, Op. 90
1809-1847

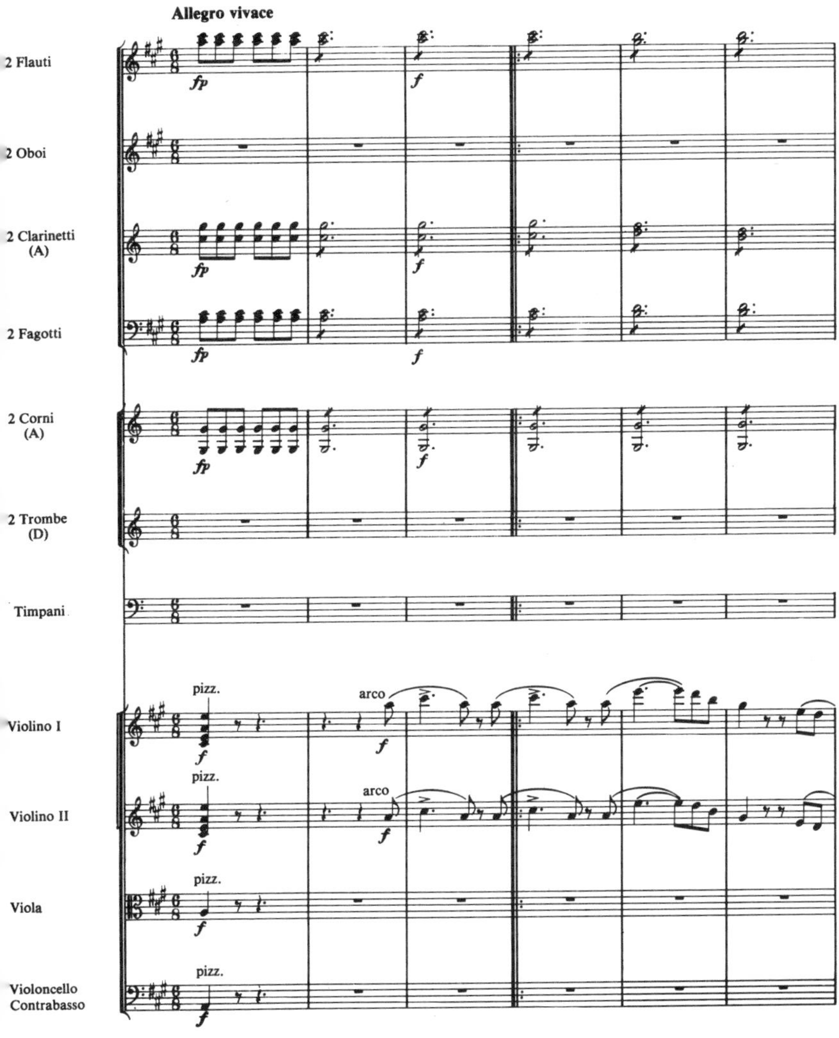

EE 6723

Ernst Eulenburg Ltd

7
Fl.
Cl.
(A)
Fg.
Cor.
(A)
I
Vl.
II
Vla.
Vc.
Cb.
arco
arco
p
sf
cresc.
15
cresc.
p
pizz.
pizz.

23
Fl.
Ob.
Cl. (A)
Fg.
Cor. (A)
Vl. I
Vl. II
Vla.
Vc.
Cb.
I
a2
arco
p
f
31
dim.
p stacc.

39
Fl.
p
cresc.
Ob.
p
cresc.
Cl.
(A)
p
cresc.
Fg.
p
cresc.
Cor.
(A)
p
cresc.
Tr.
(D)
Timp.
I
Vl.
II
p
cresc.
cresc.
Vla.
cresc.
Vc.
p
cresc.
Cb.
p
cresc.

47
Fl.
Ob.
a2
Cl.
(A)
Fg.
Cor.
(A)
Tr.
(D)
Timp.
tr
I
Vl.
II
Vla.
Vc.
Cb.

55
Fl.
Ob.
Cl.
(A)
Fg.
Cor.
(A)
Tr.
(D)
Timp.
Vl.
I
II
Vla.
Vc.
Cb.
a2
[sf]
sf
tr

63
Fl.
Ob.
Cl.
(A)
Fg.
Cor.
(A)
Tr.
(D)
a2
Timp.
I
Vl.
II
Vla.
Vc.
Cb.

71
Fl.
Ob.
Cl.
(A)
Fg.
Cor.
(A)
Tr.
(D)
Timp.
I
Vl.
II
Vla.
Vc.
Cb.
staccato
staccato
[staccato]
tr
sf
ff

79
A
(A)
(A)
(D)
Timp.
(tr)
tr
I
Vl.
II
Vla.
Vc.
Cb.
ff
sf
f

87
Fl.
Ob.
Cl.
(A)
Fg.
Cor.
(A)
Tr.
(D)
Timp.
I
Vl.
II
Vla.
Vc.
Cb.
sf
ff sf
f pp
pp
p
staccato
staccato
staccato

95
sempre staccato
sempre pp e staccato
103
pizz.
111
Vla.
Vc.
Cb.

118
Fl.
Ob.
Cl.
Fg.
I
Vl.
II
Vla.
Vc.
Cb.
p
p
p
125
Fl.
Ob.
Cl.
I
Vl.
II
Vc.
Cb.

132
b.
or.
A)
r.
D)
imp.
I
Vl.
II
la.
Vc.
Cb.
cresc.
mf
pp
p
a2
tr
arco

140
Fl.
Ob.
Cl.
(A)
Fg.
Cor.
(A)
Tr.
(D)
Timp.
I
Vl.
II
Vla.
Vc.
Cb.
149
Cl.
(A)
I Solo
I
Vl.
II
Vla.
Vc.
Cb.

159
Fl.
Ob.
Cl. (A)
I
cresc.
cresc.
Fg.
pp
cresc.
Cor. (A)
Tr. (D)
Timp.
Vl.
I
II
cresc.
f
p
cresc.
f
Vla.
p
cresc.
Vc.
cresc.
Cb.
pizz.

167
B
Fl.
Ob.
Cl.
(A)
Fg.
Cor.
(A)
Tr.
(D)
Timp.
I
Vl.
II
Vla.
Vc.
Cb.
arco
cresc.

175
Fl.
Ob.
Cl. (A)
Fg.
Cor. (A)
ff
Tr. (D)
ff
Timp.
ff
I
Vl.
II
Vla.
Vc.
Cb.

183
Fl.
Ob.
Cl.
(A)
Fg.
Cor.
(A)
Tr.
(D)
Timp.
Vl.
I
II
Vla.
Vc.
Cb.
a2
I
pizz.
192
div.
arco

200
Ob.
I
Vl.
II
Vla.
Vc.
Cb.
cresc. al f
208
Fl.
Ob.
Cl.
(A)
Fg.
Cor.
(A)
Tr.
(D)
Timp.
fp
p
sf
pizz.
arco
f

215
Ob.
Cl.
(A)
Fg.
Cor.
(A)
I
Vl.
II
Vla.
Vc.
Cb.
p
223
pp

230
Ob.
pp
Cl.
(A)
pp
Fg.
pp
Tr.
(D)
pp
Timp.
pp
I
Vl.
II
Vla.
p
237
I
Vl.
II
Vla.
Vc.
Cb.
p

244
Vl.
I
II
Vla.
Vc.
Cb.
sempre pp
sempre pp
sempre pp
sempre pp
251
cresc.
cresc.
cresc.
cresc.
258
mf
cresc.
mf
cresc.
mf
cresc.
mf
cresc.
mf
cresc.

265
a2
a2
a2
a2
a2
mp.
I
II
cresc.
cresc.
cresc.
cresc.
cresc.

273
Fl.
Ob.
Cl.
(A)
Fg.
Cor.
(A)
Tr.
(D)
Timp.
Vl.
I
II
Vla.
Vc.
Cb.
a2
f
sf
tr

281
C
Fl.
Ob.
Cl.
(A)
Fg.
Cor.
(A)
Tr.
(D)
Timp.
I
Vl.
II
Vla.
Vc.
Cb.
ff
sf
a2
tr
f

289
Ob.
Cor. (A)
Tr. (D)
Timp.
I
Vl.
II
Vla.
Vc. Cb.
f
tr
297
Fl.
Ob.
Cl. (A)
Fg.
Cor. (A)
Tr. (D)
Timp.
I
Vl.
II
Vla.
Vc. Cb.
ff

305
Cl.
A)
Cor.
(A)
Tr.
D)
I
Vl.
II
Vc.
Cb.
f

313
Fl.
Ob.
Cl.
(A)
Fg.
Cor.
(A)
Tr.
(D)
Timp.
I
Vl.
II
Vla.
Vc.
Cb.
ff
sf

321
ff
sf
I
II

329
Fl.
Ob.
Cl.
(A)
Fg.
Cor.
(A)
Tr.
(D)
Timp.
I
Vl.
II
Vla.
Vc.
Cb.
p
p
p
sf
sf
p

337
I
pp
346
I
cresc.
355
I
p
cresc.
I
mf cresc.
pp
poco a poco cresc.
p cresc.
p
poco a poco cresc.
cresc.
pp
poco a poco cresc.

363
D
Fl.
Ob.
Cl. (A)
Fg.
Cor. (A)
Tr. (D)
Vl. I
Vl. II
Vla.
Vc.
Cb.
I
a2
f
sf
mf
cresc.
371
Fl.
Ob.
Fg.
Cor. (A)
Tr. (D)
a2
Vl. I
Vl. II
Vla.
Vc. Cb.
sf

380
Fl.
Cl. (A)
Fg.
Cor. (A)
Vl. I II
Vla.
Vc. Cb.
cresc.
p
sf
387
Ob.
a2
mf

395
Fl.
Cl. (A)
Fg.
Cor. (A)
Vl. I
Vl. II
pp
402
Fl.
I
p
Cl. (A)
Fg.
Vl. I
Vla.
mf
Vc.
pizz.
Cb.
410
Fl.
Cl. (A)
Fg.
Vla.
f
Vc.
Cb.

418
Fl.
Ob.
Cl. (A)
Fg.
Vl. I
Vl. II
Vla.
Vc.
Cb.
pizz.
427
Fl.
Ob.
Cl. (A)
Fg.
Cor. (A)
Tr. (D)
Timp.
Vl. I
Vl. II
Vla.
Vc.
Cb.
a2
cresc.
arco
al

435
E
Fl.
Ob.
Cl.
(A)
Fg.
dim.
Cor.
(A)
Tr.
(D)
Timp.
I
Vl.
II
Vla.
Vc.
Cb.
dim.
dim.
dim.
dim.
dim.

445
Fl.
Cl. (A)
Fg.
Cor. (A)
Vl. I II
Vla.
Vc. Cb.
p
dim.
pp
457
Ob.

464
Fl.
Ob.
Cl. (A)
Fg.
Cor. (A)
Tr. (D)
pp
Timp.
pp
Vl. I
Vla.
470
Fl.
Ob.
cresc.
Cl. (A)
cresc.
a2
Fg.
cresc.
Cor. (A)
Tr. (D)
Vl. I
Vl. II
p
Vla.
p
Vc.
p

476
1.
b.
.)
g.
or.
A)
.)
mp.
I
II
a.
.
p
cresc.
[sempre stacc.]
[sempre stacc.]

483
Fl.
Ob.
Cl.
(A)
Fg.
Cor.
(A)
Tr.
(D)
Timp.
I
Vl.
II
Vla.
Vc.
Cb.
cresc.
tr

491
Fl.
Ob.
Cl.
(A)
Fg.
Cor.
(A)
a2
Tr.
(D)
Timp.
tr
I
Vl.
II
Vla.
Vc.
Cb.
ff
f

più animato poco a poco
499
Fl.
Ob.
Cl.
(A)
Fg.
Cor.
(A)
Tr.
(D)
Timp.
I
Vl.
II
Vla.
Vc.
Cb.
ff

F
507
l.
Ob.
Cl.
(A)
g.
Cor.
(A)
Tr.
(D)
Timp.
ff
I
Vl.
II
Vla.
Vc.
Cb.
staccato
fp dim.
p e leggiero
pizz.
515
Fl.
Fg.
I
sempre stacc. e p
div.

523
I
Fl.
Ob.
Fg.
Vl.
I
II
Vla.
Vc.
Cb.
p
cresc.
tr
531
Cl.
(A)
Cor.
(A)
Tr.
(D)
Timp.
mf
sempre cresc.
arco

539
cresc.
f
ff
or.
A)
a2
cresc.
(tr)
tr
imp.
I
II
la.
sf
f
cresc.
ff
c.
b.

547
Fl.
Ob.
Cl.
(A)
Fg.
Cor.
(A)
Tr.
(D)
Timp.
(tr)
I
Vl.
II
Vla.
Vc.
Cb.
sf
p
fp

555
I
p
a2
Vl.
II
Vla.
Vc.
Cb.

563
Fl.
Ob.
Cl.
(A)
Fg.
Cor.
(A)
Tr.
(D)
Timp.
I
Vl.
II
Vla.
Vc.
Cb.
cresc.
a2
[f]

571
Fl.
Ob.
Cl.
(A)
Fg.
Cor.
(A)
Tr.
(D)
a2
Timp.
tr
Vl.
I
II
Vla.
Vc.
Cb.
ff
sf

579
Fl.
Ob.
Cl.
(A)
Fg.
Cor.
(A)
Tr.
(D)
Timp.
I
Vl.
II
Vla.
Vc.
Cb.
sf
ff

II

Andante con moto
2 Flauti
2 Oboi
2 Clarinetti (A)
2 Fagotti
2 Corni (A)
Violino I
Violino II
Viola
Violoncello e Contrabasso
a2
I
[sim.]
Fl.
Ob.
Fg.
Vl.
Vla.
Vc. Cb.

12
Fl. I II
Vl. I II
Vc. Cb.
sempre staccato e p
18
Fl. I II
Ob. I
p
cresc.
sf
p
Fg. a2
p
cresc.
sf
p
Vl. I II
Vla.
p
cresc.
sf
p
Vc. Cb.
sempre p

24
30
I
II
a2
cresc.
sf
p

36
I
Vl.
II
[sempre stacc.]
Vla.
[sempre stacc.]
Vc.
Cb.
[sempre stacc.]
42
A
Cl.
(A)
Soli
Cor.
(A)
Vl.
Vla.
Vc.
Cb.

47
I
II
I
II
a.
52
I
II
I
II
a.
sf
p
dim.
cresc.
f

B
57
I
Fl.
II
a2
Ob.
a2
Fg.
I
Vl.
II
Vla.
Vc.
Cb.
ff
p
sfp
sf dim.
63
sf
a2
sempre p

69
I
tr
dim.
I
II
p
dim.
74
C
Fl.
sf
Ob.
Cl.
(A)
Fg.
Cor.
(A)
mf
Vl.
Vla.
Vc.
Cb.
pp

79
Fl.
I
II
Cl.
(A)
I
II
Cor.
(A)
Vl.
I
II
Vla.
Vc.
Cb.
84
dim.
Cb.

90
Fl. I
II
Ob.
a2
Fg.
a2
mf
Vl. I
II
Vla.
Vc.
Cb.
sf
dim.
96
Fl. I
II
Ob.
I
Fg.
I
pp
Vl. I
II
Vla.
Vc.
Cb.
p
dim.
pizz.

III

Con moto moderato
2 Flauti
2 Oboi
2 Clarinetti (A)
2 Fagotti
2 Corni (E)
2 Trombe (E)
Timpani
Violino I
Violino II
Viola
Violoncello
Contrabasso
6
Cor. (E)
Vl. I II
Vla.
Vc.
Cb.

14
Cor.
(E)
I
II
Vla.
21
cresc.

29
Ob.
Vl.
I
II
Vla.
Vc.
Cb.
dim.
37
Fl.
Ob.
a2
Cl.
(A)
Fg.
Cor.
(E)
Vl.
I
II
Vla.
Vc.
Cb.
cresc.

45
a2
I
II
53
a2
I
tr
I
II

61
I
Fl.
Ob.
Cl.
(A)
Fg.
Cor.
(E)
Vl.
I
II
Vla.
Vc.
Cb.
tr
p
69
cresc.
pp
dim.
pizz.

77
I
Fl.
Soli
Fg.
p
pp
Soli
Cor. (E)
p
Vl. I
pp
84
I
Fl.
Fg.
cresc.
sf
p
p
Cor. (E)
cresc.
sf
p
93
Fg.
mf
Cor. (E)
mf
Tr. (E)
mf
Timp.
mf
Vl. I
mf
Vl. II
arco
mf
Vla.
mf
Vc. Cb.
arco
mf

100
Cor. (E)
cresc.
Tr. (E)
cresc.
f
Timp.
cresc.
f
Vl. I
cresc.
f
II
cresc.
f
Vla.
cresc.
f
Vc. Cb.
f
108
Fl.
I
pp
tr
Fg.
p dolce
Cor. (E)
p dolce
Tr. (E)
Timp.
Vl. I
pp
II
Vla.
Vc. Cb.
pp
pizz.

(tr)
I
116
Fl.
Fg.
cresc.
sf
p
p
Cor. (E)
cresc.
sf
p
Vl. I
Vc. Cb.
arco
p
125
I
Vl.
II
Vla.
Vc.
Cb.
p
132
Cor. (E)
I
Vl.
II
Vla.
Vc.
Cb.

140
Fl.
I
p
Ob.
mf
Cl.
(A)
Fg.
Cor.
(E)
Tr.
(E)
Timp.
Vl.
I
II
cresc.
Vla.
Vc.
Cb.

148
Ob.
Vl.
I
II
Vla.
Vc.
Cb.
sf
cresc.
155
p
f
dim.
162
Fl.
Ob.
Cl.
(A)
Fg.
a2
f
p
cresc.

169
Fl.
Ob.
Cl. (A)
Fg.
Cor. (E)
a2
I
Vl.
II
Vla.
Vc. Cb.
177
Fl.
Ob.
a2
Cl. (A)
Fg.
I
Vl.
II
Vla.
Vc. Cb.

185
Fl.
Ob.
Cl. (A)
Fg.
Cor. (E)
Tr. (E)
Timp.
Vl.
I
II
Vla.
Vc.
Cb.
p
tr

193
Fl.
p cresc.
Ob.
Cl. (A)
p cresc.
Fg.
p cresc.
Cor. (E)
p cresc.
Tr. (E)
Timp.
Vl.
I
II
dim.
p
Vla.
Vc.
Cb.

201
Ob.
Timp.
I
Vl.
II
Vla.
Vc.
Cb.
pizz.
arco
pp
p

208
Fl.
Ob.
I
Cl.
(A)
p
Fg.
dim.
Cor.
(E)
dim.
Tr.
(E)
Timp.
I
Vl.
II
p
Vla.
Vc.
Cb.

216
1.
Ob.
Cl.
(A)
Fg.
Cor.
(E)
Tr.
(E)
Timp.
I
Vl.
II
Vla.
Vc.
Cb.
p
pp
tr
dim.
pizz.

IV

Saltarello, Presto
2 Flauti
2 Oboi
2 Clarinetti (A)
2 Fagotti
2 Corni (E)
2 Trombe (E)
Timpani
Violino I
Violino II
Viola
Violoncello e Contrabasso
tr
a2
f
ff

4
p leggiero
I
II
f
dim.
p
pp
8
tr
12
fp

16
Fl.
Ob.
Cl. (A)
Fg.
I
Cor. (E)
Vl. II
Vla.
Vc.
20
Fl.
Ob.
Cl. (A)
Fg.
a2
I
Cor. (E)
Tr. (E)
a2
Timp.
I
Vl.
II
Vla.
Vc.

24
cresc.
cresc.
cresc.
cresc.
cresc.
Imp.
tr
I
II
cresc.
cresc.
Vla.
cresc.
cresc.
p cresc.

28
Fl.
Ob.
Cl.
(A)
Fg.
Cor.
(E)
Tr.
Timp.
I
Vl.
II
Vla.
Vc.
Cb.
cresc.
al
ff
a2

32
tr
Cor.
(E)
I
II
Vla.
Vc.
Cb.
ff
36
Ob.
Cl.
A)
Fg.
(E)
Vl.
Vla.
Vc.
Cb.
f sf
sf

41
Fl.
Ob.
Cl. (A)
Fg.
Tr. (E)
a2
[f]
Timp.
Vl. I
Vl. II
Vla.
Vc. Cb.
45
a2
Fl.
Ob.
Cl. (A)
Fg.
Timp.
Vl. I
Vl. II
Vla.
Vc. Cb.

50
A
Fl.
Ob.
Cl. (A)
Fg.
Cor. (E)
Tr. (E)
Timp.
Vl. I II
Vla.
Vc. Cb.
ff
stacc.
p
I
55

59
Ob.
I
Cl.
(A)
I
Tr.
(E)
Vl.
I
II
div.
Vla.
Vc.
Cb.
64
Fl.
p
Cl.
(A)
Fg.
sf

69
Fl.
Cl.
A)
Fg.
I
Vl.
II
Vla.
Vc.
Cb.
sf p
sf
p
74
Fl.
leggiero
stacc.
pizz.
p

78
Fl.
Ob.
Cl.
(A)
Fg.
Cor.
(E)
Vl.
I
II
Vla.
Vc.
Cb.
tr
cresc.
p
82
a2
ff
Tr.
(E)
f
sf
arco

88
a2
a2
a2
ff
Timp.
I
II
3

93
Fl.
Ob.
Cl.
(A)
Fg.
Cor.
(E)
Tr.
(E)
Timp.
I
Vl.
II
Vla.
Vc.
Cb.
ff
ff
ff

98
B
a2
a2
sf
Timp.
I
Vl.
II
Vla.
Vc.
Cb.

103
Fl.
Ob.
Cl.
(A)
Fg.
Cor.
(E)
Tr.
(E)
Timp.
tr
p leggiero
Vl.
I
II
ff
sf
dim.
Vla.
Cb.
107
Fl.
Cl.
(A)
Vl.
I
II
p

111
I
II
115
p
pp
sf
tr
I
II
Vla.
119
dim.
pp
I
Vla.
Vc.
Cb.

124
Vl.
I
II
pp
Vla.
Vc.
Cb.
128
p
132
p

136
tr
I
II
a.
c.
b.
140
I
II
p
p sempre
a.
c.
b.
144
g.
I
p
I
II
la.
3
3
3
Vc.
Cb.

148
Fl.
Ob.
Cl.
(A)
Fg.
I
Vl.
II
Vla.
Vc.
Cb.
152

C
156
p
I
II
Vla.
160
cresc.
a2
Fg.
Timp.
Vl.
Vla.
Vc.
Cb.

164
Fl.
Ob.
Cl. (A)
Fg.
Cor. (E)
Timp.
Vl. I
Vl. II
Vla.
Vc. Cb.
[m]f
cresc.
a2
f
168
a2

172
Fl.
Ob.
Cl.
(A)
Fg.
Cor.
(E)
I
Vl.
II
Vla.
Vc.
Cb.
176
Fl.
Ob.
Cl.
(A)
Fg.
Cor.
(E)
Tr.
(E)
I
Vl.
II
Vla.
Vc.
Cb.

180
Fl.
Ob.
Cl.
(A)
ff
Fg.
ff
Cor.
(E)
Tr.
(E)
Timp.
ff
I
Vl.
II
Vla.
Vc.
Cb.
3

184
Ob.
Cl. (A)
Fg.
Cor. (E)
Tr. (E)
Timp.
I
Vl.
II
Vla.
Vc. Cb.

189
D
Fl.
Ob.
Cl. (A)
Fg.
Cor. (E)
Tr. (E)
Timp.
Vl. I II
Vla.
Vc. Cb.
ff
f
a2
fp
196
Cl. (A)
Fg
I
p
Cor. (E)
Tr. (E)
dim.
[p]
Timp.
Vla.
Vc.
Cb.

200
Cl. (A)
I
Fg.
Timp.
Vl. II
p
Vla.
Vc.
Cb.
204
Fl.
p
cresc.
Cl. (A)
I
Fg.
a2
Cor. (E)
p cresc.
Timp.
cresc.
I
Vl.
II
p
cresc.
cresc.
Vla.
cresc.
Vc.
cresc.
Cb.
cresc.

208
Fl.
Ob.
Cl.
(A)
Fg.
Cor.
(E)
Tr.
(E)
Timp.
Vl.
I
II
Vla.
Vc.
Cb.
mf [cresc.]
f
f
a2
p cresc.
f cresc.
più f
f
più f
f cresc.
più f
[f] cresc.

212
Fl.
Ob.
a2
Cl. (A)
Fg.
Cor. (E)
sempre cresc.
Tr. (E)
sempre cresc.
Timp.
tr
Vl.
I
II
cresc.
Vla.
cresc.
Vc. Cb.
sempre cresc. al ff

217
Fl.
Ob.
Cl.
(A)
Fg.
Cor.
(E)
Tr.
(E)
tr
tr
Timp.
I
Vl.
II
Vla.
Vc.
Cb.

221
Fl.
Ob.
a2
f
Cl.
A)
Fg.
a2
f
Cor.
(E)
Tr.
(E)
Timp.
I
Vl.
II
f
f
Vla.
f
Vc.
Cb.
f
225
Ob.
a2
f
Cl.
(A)
a2
f
a2
Fg.
f
Cor.
(E)
Tr.
(E)
Timp.
I
Vl.
II
Vla.
Vc.
Cb.

229
Fl.
Ob.
Cl.
(A)
Fg.
Cor.
(E)
Tr.
(E)
Timp.
I
Vl.
II
Vla.
Vc.
Cb.
tr
f

E
234
Fl.
Ob.
Cl.
(A)
Fg.
Cor.
(E)
Tr.
(E)
Timp.
I
Vl.
II
Vla.
Vc.
Cb.
sf
mf
p
f

240
Fl.
Ob.
Cl. (A)
Fg.
Cor. (E)
Tr. (E)
Timp.
Vl. I
II
Vla.
Vc.
Cb.
dim.
mf[dim.]
p
a2

246
Fl.
Ob.
Cl. (A)
Fg.
Cor. (E)
Timp.
Vl. I
Vl. II
Vla.
Vc. Cb.
dim.
I
p
pizz.
252
pp
Soli
legg.

256
Fl.
Ob.
Cl. (A)
Fg.
Timp.
Vl. I
p
pp
cresc.
260
Cor. (E)
Tr. (E)
Vl.
I
II
Vla.
Vc. Cb.
arco
tr
f